_____

and

Me

AND

The Story of My Broken Heart

By

_____

_____

(date)

1

Our Story - Contents

Bereaved People Are Like Ducks

Above The Surface ...
Looking Composed &
Unruffled,

Below The Surface ...
Paddling Like Crazy!

Quack!! I'm Just Ducky!!

Image Courtesy of Freepik

Grief is Like an Onion

AN ONION . . .

YOU PEEL IT

ONE LAYER AT A TIME

AND

YOU CRY A LOT . . .

Tears on the outside
Fall to the ground and

are slowly swept away.

Tears on the inside

Fall on the soul and

stay, and stay, and

stay.

Silent Hurting Heart Poem

"Oh, nothing's wrong," she smiled
and said, grinning from ear to ear.
The frown that just was on her face
seemed to disappear.

But deep down where secrets are kept,
the pain began to swell.
All the hurt inside of her
just seemed to stay and dwell.

She'd duck into the bathrooms
and hide inside the stalls,
because no one could see her tears
behind those dirty walls.

All the pain in her heart
was too much for her to take.
Pretending everything's O.K.
is much too hard to fake.

She was sick and tired of loosing
and things never turning out right.
She had no hope left in her.
She was ready to give up the fight.

She wiped away the teardrops,
put a smile back on her face,
pulled herself together, and
walked out of that place.

Life went on and things got better.
She thought that was a start.
But still no one could see inside
her silent hurting heart.

By Dayna Erickson, Seventh Grade Student, May 2, 1991

My Silent Hurting Heart

My heart is broken because _____ died on _____

                                (Write the name.)   (Write the date.)

This is my broken heart.

Grief is what I feel inside when someone I love dies. I also feel grief when I am separated from anyone or anything that is important to me. It's a lot of work putting a broken heart back together. (It's called "griefwork!") It can take a long time.

My heart will never be quite the same.

All About Me...

My name is _____. I'm in grade _____

at_____ (school). I was born _____ (month/day/year).

I live with_____ in_____.
            (names of people)   (city/state)

I am_____tall. I have_____hair and_____eyes.
    (feet & inches)   (your hair length & color)   (your eye color)

I like to wear_____. My favorite color is_____.

My favorite food(s) is/are:_____,

My pets are: _____.

My favorite song and/or singing group is: _____

_____.

My favorite movie is: _____.

My best friend is:_____.

At school I like: _____.

In my free time I like to:_____.

On weekends I usually:_____.

This summer I want to:_____.

Someday I want:_____.

I feel good when: _____.

Meet My_____

(Write title and his or her name.)

I will always love_____. I will never forget_____.

These are things that I will always remember about_____.
(Make a list or draw a picture.)

Eventually, if I do my griefwork, when I think of_____,

it won't hurt so much.

Favorite Things

Here's a list of _____**'s favorite:**

People_____

Place to visit/vacation_____

Color_____ Animal _____

Foods _____

Flowers/Fragrance_____

Car/Transportation_____

Free time activity_____

Sport/Team_____

Music/Music Group_____

Radio Station_____

Movie/Movie Star_____

T.V. Program_____

His/her Pet Peeve_____

Acrostic Example

D – drummer of "Wipe Out"
O – oldest child
N – nutty and fun

P – patient with baby sister

A – always played games/cards to win

U – under tall to suit his taste

L – loved to drive circles in the Bartel's car

E – eager to play basketball or baseball

R – really good friend to Lou & Aaron

I – irritated with his brother

C – courageous in battling cancer

K – kind to animals and little kids

S – sure to have the last word

O – often his dad's pal

N – nice to have around

You will always be my precious __son__.

I love you, _Donny_. _Mom_ **Nov. 14, 2000**
(signature) (date)

An Acrostic for _____.

Write your loved one's name in a column down the left side of this page. Then think of words or phrases that describe him or her which start with those letters.

Alphabet Poem (Sample)

About Don Paul Erickson

By Mom

A

Beloved

Child

Donny was

Every thing a parent could want in a child

Frequent talks

Genuinely likable

Had lots of enthusiasm for life

Involved in sports

Just any game with a ball

Kind to animals

Loved to be in the front of the line

Made lots of friends

Never complained about being sick

Once he ran the Sound to Narrows with Dad

Probably never kissed a girl

Quiet in his last days

Really good drummer

Small for his age

Tried hard to play well

Unfinished business of living

Valued his family & friends

Wanted to win every game

X-rays revealed the tumor

You will always be loved

Z until the end of time

Alphabet Poem

About _____

By _____

_____
(date)

A		N	
B		O	
C		P	
D		Q	
E		R	
F		S	
G		T	
H		U	
I		V	
J		W	
K		X	
L		Y	
M		Z	

My Personal Experience with Death

When I think about death _____

_____

When I think about my _____ 's death, I wonder _____

_____

What makes it difficult to talk about death is _____

_____

One way my life has changed because of the death is _____

One of my favorite memories of being with my _____is

_____

At the funeral I _____

One thing I wish my teachers understood is _____

_____

I wish my friends would _____

I would like my mom and dad to know _____

The biggest change since _____ died is _____

_____

It isn't easy for me to admit _____

One of my greatest fears is _____

When I'm feeling really sad, it helps me to _____

_____

About the Death

Write what you know (or draw a picture) about how your loved one died.

Funeral/Memorial Service

For_____,

(Write his or her name.)

It was held on _____ at _____.

(date)   (name of place it was held)

Who was there? Family_____.

Friends _____.

If you didn't attend, tell why_____.

What stands out in your mind about the service?

_____.

What music was played?

_____.

Who spoke?_____.

What did you like about the service? _____.

_____.

What part was hard for you? _____.

What would you change? _____.

_____was_____. His/Her_____

(Name or He/She)   (buried or cremated)   (remains or cremains)

are now located at _____. After the service

_____.

"Gone from my presence, ever present in my heart."

We Remember Them

A Responsorial Poem

At the rising of the sun and its going down
We remember them.

At the blowing of the wind and the chill of winter,
We remember them.

At the opening of the buds and the rebirth of spring,
We remember them.

At the shining of the sun and in the warmth of summer,
We remember them.

At the rustling of the leaves and in the beauty of autumn,
We remember them.

At the beginning of the year and at its end,
We remember them.

As long as we live, they too will live; for they are now a part of us, as
We remember them.

When we are weary and in need of strength,
We remember them.

When we are lost and sick at heart,
We remember them.

When we have joy we crave to share,
We remember them.

When we have decisions that are difficult to make,
We remember them.

When we have achievements that are based on theirs,
We remember them.

As long as we live, they too will live; for they are now a part of us, as
We remember them.

A Litany of Remembrance Poem by Rabbi Sylvan Kamens and Rabbi Jack Riemer.
© Central Conference of American Rabbis. Used by kind permission of the CCAR.

My Grief Bundle

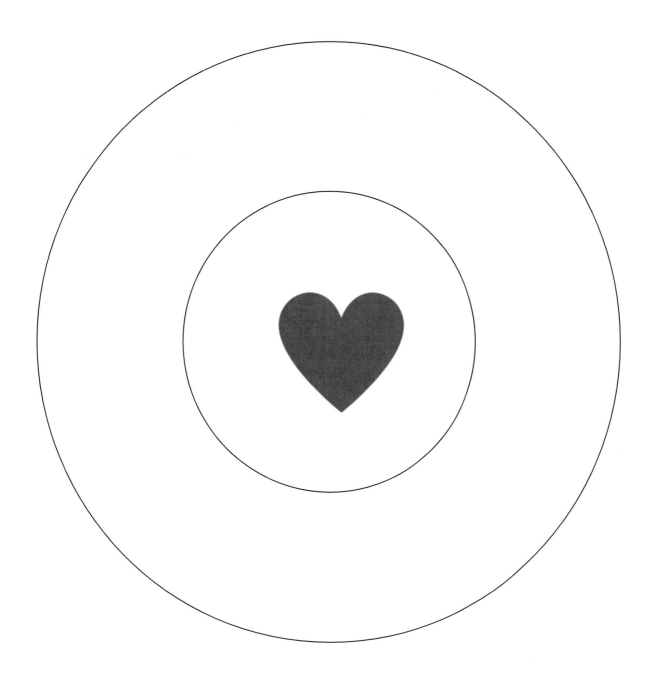

Everyone has a grief bundle of all the separations and losses experienced since birth. Here is mine. With each new loss I might feel the grief of my *whole* grief bundle. A *part* or *all* of my grief bundle may "recycle" as a "grief attack." This may explain my <u>big</u> reactions to little losses!
It will also probably recycle when I am a teenager.

We Will Light Candles

We Will Light Candles

Candles of joy despite all sadness

Candles of hope where despair keeps watch

Candles of courage for fears ever present

Candles of peace for tempest-tossed days

Candles of graces to ease heavy burdens

Candles of love to inspire all our living

Candles that will burn all year long

Author Unknown

The Pain of Grief

Sometimes I physically feel the pain of grief. This is where and how I feel it in my body

Watermelon Hugs

Sometimes I'm sad;
I mean very-very sad.
Sometimes I'm mad;
I mean very-very mad.

Sometimes my feelings
Are in a jumbled-up way;
But my words get stuck
And I don't know what to say.

I need a secret word
That I can softly say
To let my people know
"I need some hugs today."

There's *flipper-flap* and *snipper-snap*
And *blueberry* and *baba-bee*;
But **WATERMELON** seemed just right—
It's the best secret word for me.

I shared my secret word with some
Special people--just a few---
So, when they hear **WATERMELON**,
They will know just what to do.

Now when I'm sad and want to hide
Under my fuzzy bear rug,
I just whisper **WATERMELON**,
And I get a great big HUG!

Carol Weedman Reed 2010 Printed by permission.

My Feelings of Grief

Feelings are not right or wrong. They just **are**. I *have* to "feel" my grief in order to "heal." Here are some of my feelings.
(Write words or draw pictures or both.)

Grief can make you feel like you're going crazy.

Grief Behaviors

(Mourning)

Some of my grief behaviors aren't planned. Sometimes my grief behavior just "leaks" or it may come out like a volcano or "grief vomit." These actions come from a lot of jumbled up feelings. It's OK as long as I don't hurt myself or other people. These expressions of my grief are what is called "mourning." Here are some ways I have shown my grief.

1. _____

2. _____

3. _____

4. _____

5. _____

6. _____

7. _____

8. _____

Toilet Bowl Love

(Royal Flushes)

I've written some examples of things people say and do that hurt my feelings or make me mad. I choose to flush all that.

Griefwork

To "heal" means that I will be able to remember _____ without so much pain. It means that I will enjoy living again. It does **not** mean that I will forget _____ or stop loving him/her.

Sometimes I will still miss him/her a lot. I will always love and remember _____. I will love others also. Griefwork is what I do that will help me work *through* the pain of grief. For example, I can:

It's not healthy to grieve all day. So, when I need a break from "griefwork," these are things that I can do to help myself feel better:

It may take a long time and be a lot of hard work that doesn't feel good, but *I choose to do things that will help me to heal.*

_____
(your signature)

How My Family Has Changed

Many things have changed since _____ died.

The changes I like are: The changes I don't like are:

_____   _____

_____   _____

Before _____ died, my family looked like this:

[   ]

Now my family looks like this:

[   ]

Imprints - Your Mark on My Life

When I push my finger into clay, it leaves a mark. _____
has made a mark on my life. The parts of me that may be like him/her
are:

Things I <u>have</u> or like to <u>do</u> that are like him/her are:

Marks that I do not like and want to change about me are:

I can celebrate the good marks that _____ has made on my
life. I can work at changing what I want to be different about me. I can
live so that _____ would be very proud of me. This will help my
broken heart heal. I am becoming a new and unique ME.

I will always be _____'s _____
(son, daughter, sister, etc.)

Dreams

The death of someone loved can make kids have bad or weird dreams. They may be scary or upsetting.
Draw a dream you can remember.

Bad dreams get better over time.
Draw or tell how you would change your dream.

My Circle of Support

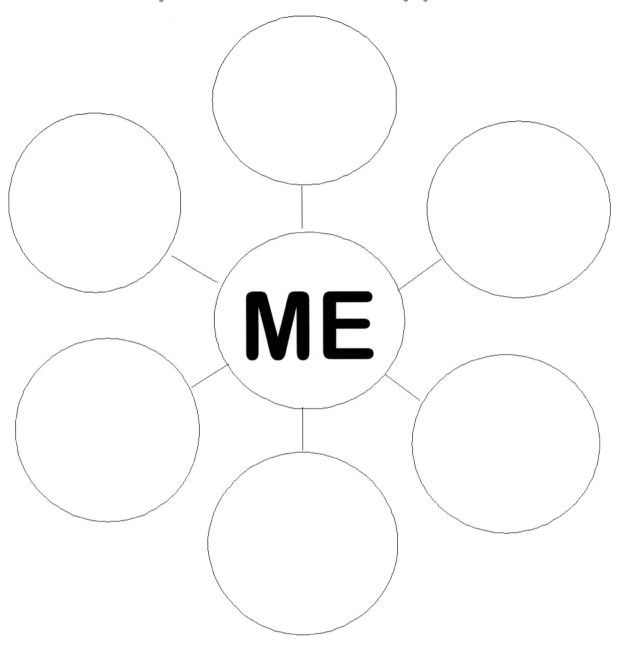

My circle of support are the people who care about me,
listen to me, and help me. Here they are.
These are the people I can talk to.

My Safe Place

Sometimes I need a quiet place where I can feel safe and be alone with my feelings. Here's a picture of my safe place.

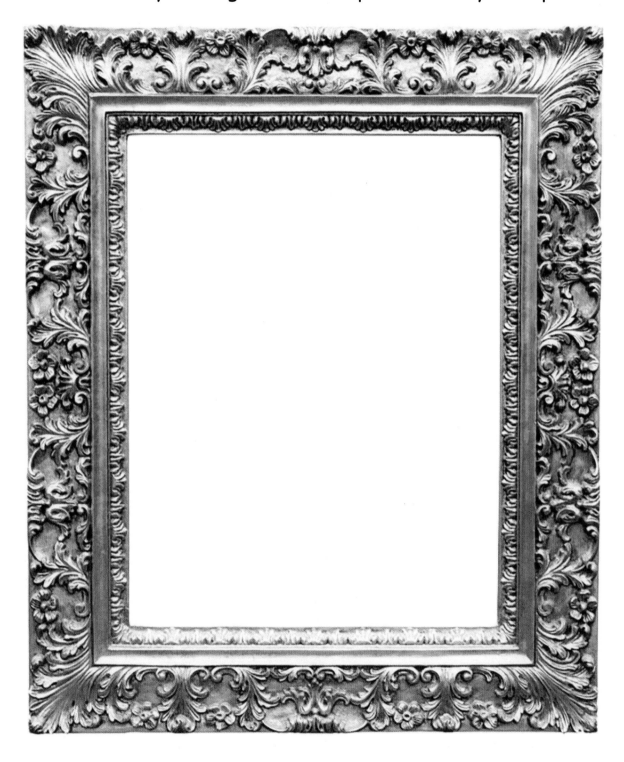

Will I Heal?

To "heal" means that I will remember _____ without hurting so much. It means that I will feel more like myself and want to do things that are fun: my life will seem good again.

To "heal" does not mean that I will forget _____ or stop loving him/her. It does not mean that I won't feel the pain of grief ever again. There will always be reminders that may make me sad. Or happy. Or both.

This is a picture of me after _____ died and how I will look someday when I've done my griefwork.

<u>After</u>   <u>Someday</u>

Bouquet of Memories

These are some of my favorite memories of

_____.

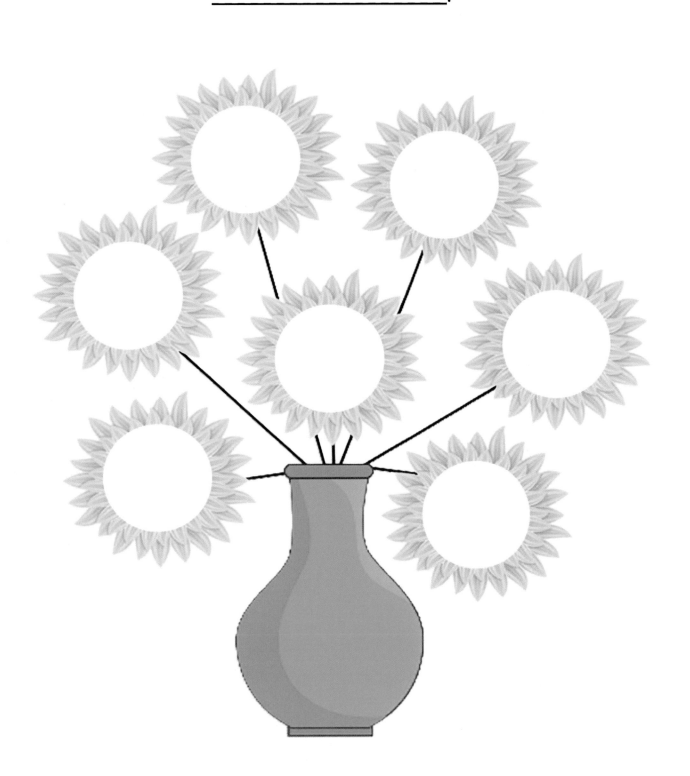

My Gratitude List

Even though I am sad when I miss _____, there are lots of things that I can be glad about. When I think about them, my heart feels lots better.

1. _____

2. _____

3. _____

4. _____

5. _____

6. _____

7. _____

8. _____

9. _____

10. _____

It is a healthy habit to add to my Gratitude List every day, even after my broken heart heals.

Treasured Memories

When someone we love dies, our memories of them become our treasure. Reach inside this treasure chest to find some memories about _____ that I treasure.

Love You Forever...

I will always love _____. These are ways that I can still show my love
for _____. (Make a list. Pick your favorite and draw a picture on the back of this page.)

1. _____

2. _____

3. _____

4. _____

5. _____

6. _____

7. _____

8. _____

9. _____

10. _____

11. _____

12. _____

A Special Letter

_____
(today's date)

Dear_____,

_____

_____

_____

_____

_____

_____

_____

_____

_____
(Your Name)

When Someone Else Has A Broken Heart...

Sometimes I can tell that someone else has a broken heart. They look sad or mad or don't want to play or talk. They might be grieving because they had to say good-bye to someone or something that they cared about, or maybe someone died. These are ways I can be a good friend to someone who is grieving. (The pictures will give you a hint.)

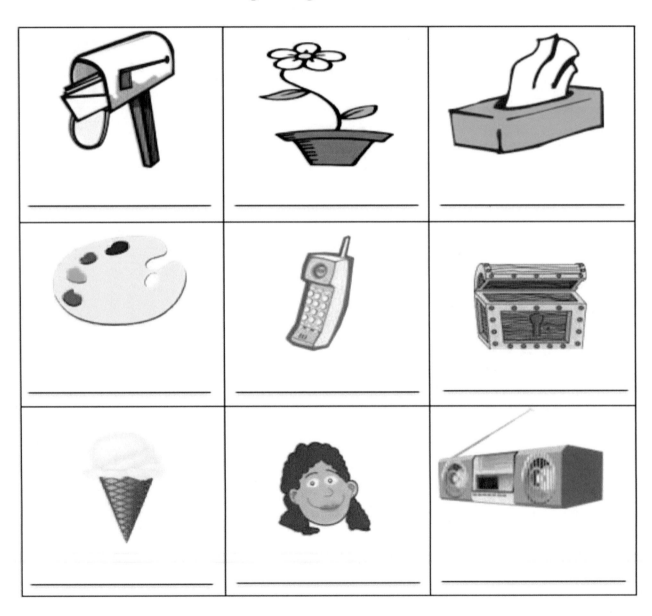

Thank You For Completing Your
Our Story Memory Book!

And

Congratulations!

You have done a lot of healing griefwork!

I would like to recommend you keep this book in a special place.

Remember how grief recycles?

When it does, your memory book will help you do griefwork again.

I suggest you revisit the pages with someone you love.

AND

You know what?

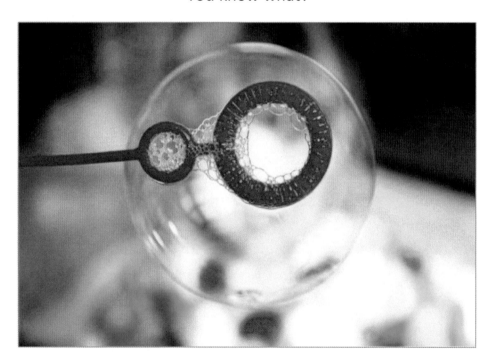

We are never too old to blow love bubbles!

Your friend,

Mel Erickson
mel@kidtalkgrief.com

In The Same Series

Kid Talk A Faith-Based Curriculum for Grieving Children Includes *Our Story*: A Memory Book

The two books are printed together for you to easily compile a support group program with over 100 healing activities for grieving kids. The comprehensive faith-based curriculum provides lesson plans, leader's guides, supply lists and supplemental materials for 14 two-hour sessions. The user-friendly format accommodates multiple learning styles, settings, and ages between 6 and 12 years old.

With the content of these two books, you will be equipped to offer comfort and healing to one child or a group of children.

- **Easily plan and implement creative and engaging activities that promote healing in a grieving child**
- **Have "kid talk" language for difficult explanations related to death**
- **Give each child a personal memory book that will help him tell his story, express, and process his feelings of grief, and not have to worry that he will forget.**
- **Know where to find supplemental materials, supplies and resources**

ISBN 978-1-7365868-0-8

Additional *Our Story* Memory Books can be purchased on Amazon:
ISBN 978-1-7365868-1-5

Essential Read In The Same Series

12 Simple Tips and Tools to Help Your Grieving Child
What I Wish I Had Known When My Son Died

This little handbook is perfect to gift to grieving caregivers who want to help a bereaved child in their life. In an easy-to-read conversational style, the author shares her story, her faith and essential insights she has learned about grieving kids over thirty years as a grief specialist.

Topics covered include:

✓ How to Break Bad News to a Child

✓ Is my Child's Grief Normal?

✓ How Can I Help My Grieving Child?

✓ Should My Child Come to the Remembrance Service?

✓ What Words Do I Use to Explain…

This book is part of the **Kid Talk Grief Series**, and is a companion read to
Kid Talk A Faith-Based Curriculum for Grieving Children Including *Our Story* **Memory Book.**

Available as a paperback and an eBook on Amazon
Paperback ISBN - 978-736-5868-3-9
eBook ISBN – 978-1-7365868-2-2

Copyright Information
Our Story Memory Book

Printed in the United States of America by Amazon KDP.
First Edition - 2021.

ISBN – 987-1-7365868-1-5

www.kidtalkgrief.com

Made in the USA
Coppell, TX
08 March 2023

13976616R00026